D0581734
POLAND
ZECHOSLOVAKIA
A
HUNGARY
RUMANIA
YUGOSLAVIA
BULGARIA
BLACK SEA
ALBANIA
GREECE
TURKEY
ATHENS
SYRIA
CYPRUS
MEDITERRANEAN
SEA
DAMASCUS
LYDDA
JERUSALEM
JORDAN
Suez
Canal
RED SEA
5 p.

Series 587

Fly with Alison and John to Israel and—through the pictures and story in this book—see with them the wonders of the Holy Land. Visit the Crusader castles, the Sea of Galilee, the Dead Sea, Jerusalem and Nazareth—where Jesus lived as a boy.

In this wonderful land of the Bible—the home of the tribes of Israel and the setting of the New Testament—a new nation is being built.

A LADYBIRD
TRAVEL ADVENTURE
BOOK

2/6
NET

FLIGHT SIX:

THE HOLY LAND

by
DAVID SCOTT DANIELL

with illustrations by
JACK MATTHEW

Publishers: Wills & Hepworth Ltd., Loughborough

First Published 1962 © *Printed in England*

FLIGHT SIX:
THE HOLY LAND

John had the seat next to the porthole in the big plane so he looked out most of the time. Below was a carpet of puffy clouds, but when there was a gap he could see minute fields in France, and sometimes a cluster of little dots which was a town. When they were flying over Switzerland he saw the mountains and snow-capped peaks of the Alps.

Alison sat next to him and spent most of the time watching the people in the air-liner, expecially the handsome Captain and the friendly stewardess when they passed through the plane.

" John," his father said, suddenly, " what's our course? "

John thought for a moment and looked at the map in his lap. " South-east from London to Rome, and then east-south-east to Athens and on to Israel. Altogether about two-thousand-four-hundred miles."

" Correct. And Alison, here's one for you. Where is Israel? "

" Oh, well," said Alison, " it is a narrow strip of land right at the end of the Mediterranean."

" Very good. Yes, Israel is very small, but very important, and it is a wonderful land in many ways, as you will see. Jesus Christ lived there, preached, and died. It is sacred to the Jews because it is their 'Promised Land,' which God gave to the children of Israel; and Israel is sacred to the Moslems, too."

They had lunch before they got to Rome, and a splendid dinner between Athens and Israel. As the plane came in to land at Lydda Airport, Alison and John peered out to get their first glimpse of Israel—the Holy Land.

Lydda Airport

EL AL אל על

A bus ride of twelve miles took them from the airport to their hotel in Tel Aviv, and although it was late their father took them out. The streets were busy and gay, and brilliantly lighted. People strolled in the warm evening, or sat at tables in front of cafés drinking coffee. Everywhere they saw new, handsome buildings, and the streets were full of cars and taxis, buses and bicycles.

" What a busy, cheerful place it is! " Alison exclaimed.

" I'll tell you something," their Father said, " and John, you must put it in your notebook. Fifty years ago this was just barren desert! Now Tel Aviv is a city with a population of half-a-million."

" But—why, what happened? " John asked, looking round at the tall buildings and the bustle of the traffic and people.

" Well, you see, it joins Jaffa, a very ancient port."

" Ah, Jaffa oranges! " Alison said.

" That's right. They grow them in Israel and they used to ship them from Jaffa. Now they use Haifa, where we're going next. Well, fifty years ago, some people in Jaffa decided to build a new suburb outside the city, because Jaffa was old and crowded. So twenty labourers, under the direction of a watchmaker, began to build themselves houses. The place has grown and grown, especially in the past few years, and now it's Israel's newest, biggest and busiest city! "

Their father had to spend several days in Tel Aviv on business, so Alison and John were able to explore the city, and the fascinating old Jaffa, which has a history extending over four thousand years.

Night scene in Tel Aviv

BANK

Staying in Tel Aviv was great fun; the children soon learned a few words of Hebrew, including *Shalom* for "Hello!" (which really means "Peace"), *Toda* for "Thank you," and *Ken* and *Lo* for "Yes" and "No." They swam in the warm sea of the Mediterranean from a smart lido. They were sorry when their father had finished his business calls and they had to leave.

They went by train to Haifa, sixty miles to the north. It was exciting looking out of the window at the countryside, and they were often in sight of the sea.

"What are those trees?" John asked.

His father looked where John was pointing. "That's an olive grove. Olives are little, hard green fruit, used to make olive oil."

"Look, oranges!" Alison said. "An orange grove, and the oranges look like hundreds of glowing lights in the trees!"

"And there are some date palms," her father said, "and over there lemon trees."

Suddenly John stood up excitedly, and pointed out of the window. "Camels!" he said. "Arabs riding on camels!"

"That's something to remember, John," his father said. "And do you see that woman on the little donkey? That would have been just the same when Our Lord lived here, or in the days of Abraham, David and Solomon. People travelling on camels and donkeys. Now look over there—a modern tractor at work. And do you see the concrete irrigation ditch? That is the modern Israel, the ancient and historic land of the Bible being enriched and modernised. All over Israel they are making the land fertile and developing it with modern machinery."

Donkey, camels and a tractor

They spent two days in Haifa, a very clean city of white, modern buildings which climbed up the side of Mount Carmel. Haifa is Israel's main port, so they went to the docks and watched stacks of cases of oranges and lemons being loaded into ships. They saw the petrol refinery, the power stations, mills, cement works, and factories.

The residential part of the city, with its pretty villas and gardens full of flowers, is built on the slopes of Mount Carmel. They went up for a picnic. They looked down on the roofs of Haifa, the port, and the blue sea beyond.

John said, " In our atlas at home Israel is called Palestine."

" It was Palestine until 1948, John. But let me explain. In the Bible we read how the Children of Israel were brought here when Moses led them out of bondage in Egypt. The northern part was Israel and the southern part, Judea. But a hundred years after Jesus was crucified the Jews were scattered all over the world. They were homeless. Often they were cruelly persecuted."

" But why? " asked Alison.

" That's a difficult question, Alison. But always the Jews remembered the ancient promise of the prophet Ezekiel, who prophesied that the Lord God would gather them from the nations, assemble them out of the countries where they had been scattered, and give them the land of Israel."

" So that's why they call it Israel now? " Alison queried.

" Yes. In 1948 a wonderful thing happened. The United Nations gave this land back to the Jews; their ancient home. At last they have a home, and are a nation again."

The roof-tops of Haifa

From Haifa a fourteen mile drive northwards along a fine coast road took them to Acre, or Ako, as it is now called. Alison and John were enchanted with this town of white buildings, domes, and minarets, alongside the blue sea. They strolled on the old city walls.

" Acre is one of the most ancient cities in the world," their father said.

" How old? " John asked, opening his note-book.

" Well, it was an important city in 1500 B.C., John. We know that from ancient Egyptian writings, and it is mentioned in the Old Testament, too."

Alison had brought her Bible specially. " Where can I read about it? " she asked.

Her father looked at his guide book. " In Judges, Alison—that's the seventh book, chapter 1, verse 31. You'll see it's called Accho."

While Alison looked it up, John asked, " Didn't the Crusaders fight here at Acre? "

"Indeed they did, John, often. Saladin captured it in 1187, and it was recaptured by our own King Richard I, Richard Lionheart, in 1191, in the Third Crusade."

John gazed around him, imagining the din of battle and the Crusaders with their white surcoats, on which there was a big cross, over their armour.

They strolled round the town, where the streets were so narrow that they were shaded from the hot sun. In the bazaars clever craftsmen made copper and bronze vessels, silversmiths were busy with their tiny hammers, and men weaved gaily coloured cloth. They saw Arabs in white head-dresses and Jews in European clothes.

The walls of Acre

They had hired a car for the journey to Acre, and then drove eastwards across Galilee, the northern part of Israel. It was a land of rolling hills and green valleys, rich with pasture, cornlands, and orchards. It was full of places of Biblical history, which their father pointed out to them.

" This is the richest and loveliest part of Israel," he told them. " It is the land ' flowing with milk and honey ' which was promised to the Children of Israel, and given to them after their captivity in Egypt. Many of the great events in the Old Testament happened in Galilee, and it was here that Jesus lived, and began to preach."

Alison and John gazed around them wide-eyed as they drove eastwards. They stopped for a picnic lunch under a fig tree, and afterwards Alison made a sketch of the scene while John wrote up his notes.

" What have we seen to-day, John? " his father asked him.

John turned back a page of his book. " Three ruins of Crusader castles, a pair of eagles, and those gorgeous, pink flamingoes. And I've got down wheat, oats, and maize; cows and sheep; and under fruits I've got pine-apples, apricots, and vineyards full of grapes."

" You're always coming across vineyards in the Bible," Alison said. " I'm going to put some lemon trees in my picture, with lemons on." She drew for a moment or two and then she held up her hand and said, " Listen! What's that music? "

" Look, over there! " said John, pointing.

They looked and saw an Arab shepherd boy, sitting on a rock, playing a home-made pipe to himself, while his sheep grazed around him.

An Arab shepherd boy

After their picnic they drove on until their father stopped the car at the top of a hill, where they all got out. He took them to the side of the road.

" There! " he said. " The Sea of Galilee! "

Below them was a great lake, sparkling in the sunshine. It lay in a rich, green valley, with brown hills in the distance.

" If you want some facts, John," his father said, " the Sea of Galilee is a lake about twelve-and-a-half miles long and eight miles across its widest part. It is shaped like a harp, and is seven-hundred feet below sea level. It is fed by the River Jordan. But apart from these facts, it is the most famous lake in the world! "

" Because it was here that Jesus walked on the water? " Alison asked.

" And because He found His first disciples here? " queried John.

" You are both right. Peter and Andrew, and James and John were fishermen here, and Our Lord told them to follow Him. Jesus preached here by the sea, and it was at Capernaum, at the top of the lake, that He cured the Roman centurion's servant. It is in St. Matthew, Alison, chapter 8, verses 5 to 13."

They motored to the Mount of Beatitudes, where Jesus preached the 'Sermon on the Mount,' and saw the old town of Capernaum. Then they drove slowly down the road beside the sea to Tiberias, passing modern farms with up-to-date buildings and machinery, and ancient villages and old temples. They saw modern villages, too, with bathing lidos and smart restaurants. On the sea were fishing boats which might have been the same as in the time of Our Lord, and modern launches and speed-boats.

They spent four glorious days at Tiberias. They swam in the Sea of Galilee, went fishing in a boat and then went sight-seeing.

" All Israel is a place of pilgrimage to Christians and to Jews," their father explained. " And Galilee is particularly full of Biblical history. People come here from all over the world."

Alison opened her Bible, found a place and said. " Listen. I found this in St. Matthew's Gospel, chapter 4, verse 23: ' *And Jesus went about all Galilee, teaching in their synagogues, and preaching the gospel of the kingdom, and healing all manner of sickness and all manner of disease among the people.*' "

" And we're actually *here*! " John said in an awed voice.

When they left Tiberias to drive to Nazareth they turned off the main road and drove along a track they had been told about. They stopped and they got out. Some archæologists were working on the site of a vanished city. The children watched, fascinated.

" Israel is full of ancient towns, temples, and palaces," their father said, " and the archæologists find out where they were and dig very carefully into the ground. They examine all the fragments they find—stones, pottery, and metal—and from the evidence they find, they can discover about the past."

" Like the Dead Sea scrolls? " Alison asked.

"Yes. In 1947 a shepherd boy found some ancient jars hidden in a cave near the Dead Sea, and inside were Biblical writings on leather, which had been hidden away two-thousand years ago! "

" We must look too," said John, hopefully.

They drove on towards Nazareth, but stopped to have a look at the little village of Cana. It was there that Jesus changed the water into wine at the wedding feast; and, remembering this they strolled about the village, busy with their own thoughts.

They stopped again just outside Nazareth, and gazed at the famous town nestling among the hills, with it's great number of spires of churches and convents amidst the tall cypresses and the dark olives. Their hotel was a mile beyond the town, and after they had settled in they strolled back to explore Nazareth.

They stopped on the road to watch a string of camels loaded with packages, being overtaken by a modern car. It seemed quite natural.

" Here in Israel you are always seeing the ancient and the modern side by side," said their father. " And Christian, Jew, and Moslem all live peacefully together." When they were in the town he pointed to the buildings. " Look, there's a mosque, that's a Moslem church; and next to it is a synagogue, a Jewish church; and next to that a Christian church and a convent. Up the road, too, there is a Baptist Chapel."

" There seem to be more Arabs than anyone else in Nazareth," said Alison.

" It's principally an Arab town. Listen to the Arab music coming from that café, and look at the Arabs drinking coffee and smoking their hubble-bubble pipes! "

They went up a narrow street and came to an old quarter of the town which might have been just the same two-thousand years ago, when Jesus was a boy living in Nazareth.

A street in Nazareth

Alison was busy with her sketch book in Nazareth, and she had many passages to read in her Bible. John made lots of notes, and their father took a great number of photographs. They found it inspiring just to look about them and imagine Nazareth as it was two-thousand years ago.

Their father took them to see the cave which was once the home of Jesus, where Joseph had his carpenter's shop. and where Mary cooked and kept house. Another place for dreaming was the site of the Annunciation, where the Angel Gabriel appeared to Mary and told her that she was to have a son who would be called Jesus.

They stayed longest at Mary's Well, by the side of the modern road out of town. They watched the women and children filling their earthenware pitchers at the well.

" Is this really the same well that Mary used? " Alison asked, gazing at the well.

" Wells don't move," her father said. " This one has always been used so it must have been in use when Jesus was a boy."

" Then Mary must have come here! " Alison said.

" And Jesus, too," added John, " when He was big enough! "

" I wish we could drink some of this water! " said Alison.

Their father spoke to an Arab boy, and he smiled and nodded, and tipped some water from his pitcher into Alison's cupped hands and then into John's. They thanked him, drank the water, and for once neither of them had anything to say—but they had a great deal to think about.

Mary's Well in Nazareth

On their last morning in Nazareth, a friend of their father's met them at their hotel to take them to stay at a kibbutz. He was Mr. Uri Gilboa, and he brought his daughter Ilana and his son Danny with him.

In the car John said, " Mr. Gilboa, what *is* a kibbutz? "

" You can rely on John to ask questions," said his father.

" And quite right, too," Mr, Gilboa replied. "A kibbutz, John, is a special sort of village. Everyone who lives there works—for nothing! We all work a six-day week, and no one gets any pay."

" We don't work for nothing," said Danny, " we work for Israel! "

" Yes, that's the reason of it all. You see, John, we are making a new nation, so many Israelis are prepared to work for that reason alone. But it's not as hard as it sounds. Everyone gets pocket-money, a home, food, clothes, books, newspapers, and everything he needs; and a holiday every year, too."

" It's not easy to describe it," said Ilana, " but you'll soon see for yourselves."

The kibbutz was a village of modern bungalows, with pretty gardens, surrounded by fields and orchards. It was all new, busy, and exciting. Danny and Ilana took Alison round, and they saw the school and the children's houses where the young children play, study, and eat.

" It's like living for ever in a holiday-camp," Alison said. " They have everything."

" The only difference is that everyone works hard, and loves it," John said.

Before long Alison and John started work, picking oranges while their father was happily driving a tractor.

Alison and John worked with Ilana and Danny for a very happy week. From six o'clock in the morning they were out in the orchards, and they worked until four in the afternoon. The people sang as they worked, made jokes, teased each other and they all, several hundred of them, seemed to be on holiday like Alison and John. But it was not a holiday for them, it was their life, day in, day out, throughout the year.

After four o'clock came leisure. You went to the library for books or gramophone records; or you danced, or bathed, played football, or rehearsed for a play or a concert.

" This is a beautiful place," Alison said, as they lay in the sun one evening after a swim in the bathing-pool. " You've got *everything* here! "

" Yet once this was all empty marshland," Danny said. "A few people came and drained it, planted the first crops and built the first bungalows. Gradually more people came, and this is the result! Just hard work! "

" Hard work and faith in our country and its future," Ilana added.

" You see, there are two-million Israelis in a very small country, most of it undeveloped. We have to work hard to grow the food to keep us."

On Saturday evening everyone went to the open-air cinema. Alison and John lay in the grass with Ilana and Danny, in the warm-scented darkness, and they felt proud to belong, if only for a few days, to this village of a thousand friendly, hard-working and happy people.

Open air cinema

The week at the kibbutz came to an end, and Alison and John said good-bye to their Israeli friends, and all the other people they had got to know. On their way back to Haifa, they looked at other kibbutzem with especial interest. They noticed that every kind of crop was being grown, and that there were factories as well.

From Haifa they went by train, a hundred-and-fifty miles southwards, to Beersheba, the capital of the southern part of Israel, called the Negev.

" Isn't it time you drew us one of your maps? " John asked his father in the train, " marking the places where we've been? "

" And please," Alison added, " put in the places we are going to. I know! A red line to show where we've been and a black line to show where we are going."

Their father took John's notebook and thought for a minute. " Israel is an awkward shape for this page," he said. " I'll have to leave out most of the Negev in the South. It's mainly desert, and it goes down to a point at the Gulf of Elath, which goes into the Red Sea. Look, the big map shows you."

He drew a map, with part of the Lebanon, Syria, Jordan, and Egypt, the countries which surround Israel. He put in the places they had been to, with a red line to show their route, and, as Alison had asked him, a black line to show where they were going.

John said, " Draw a train to show where we are now."

So he obliged.

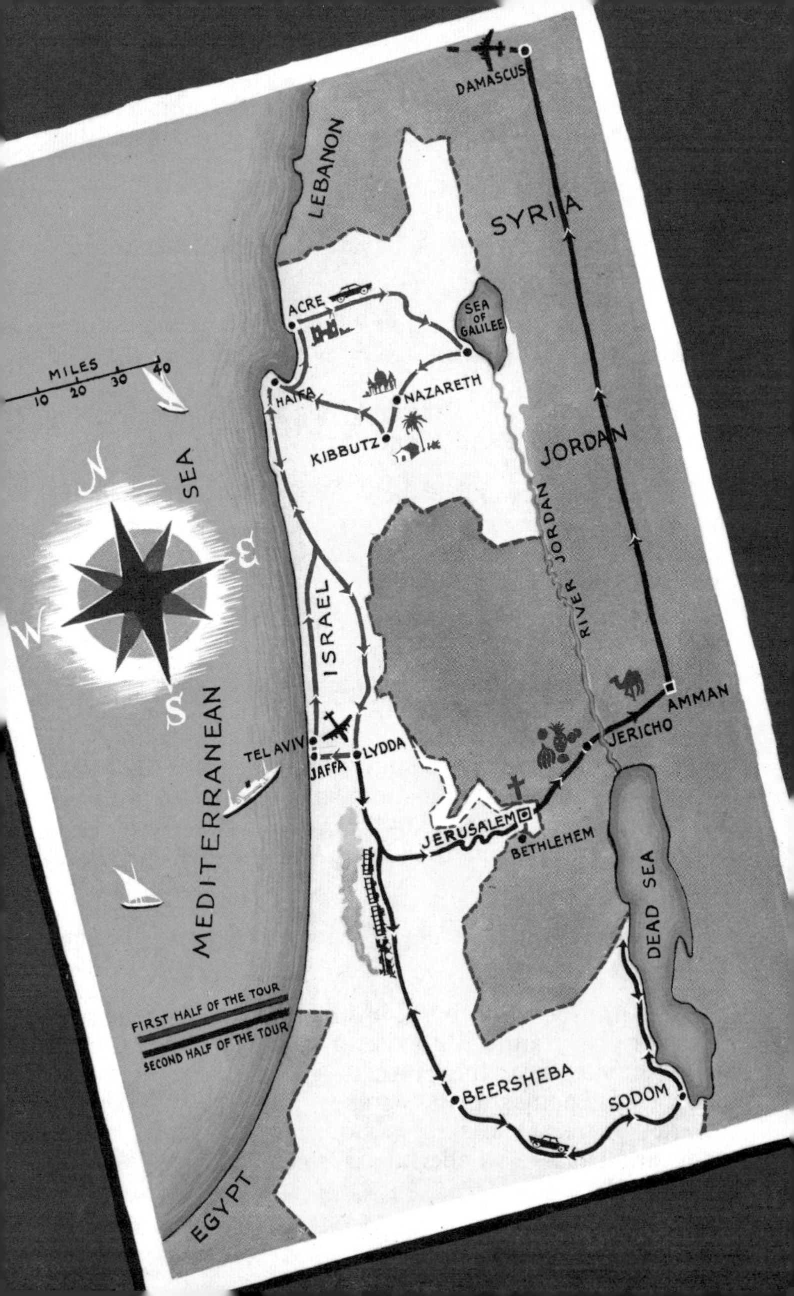
DAMASCUS
LEBANON
SYRIA
SEA OF GALILEE
ACRE
HAIFA
NAZARETH
KIBBUTZ
MILES
10
20
30
40
N
E
W
S
MEDITERRANEAN
SEA
ISRAEL
JORDAN
RIVER JORDAN
AMMAN
JERICHO
TEL AVIV
JAFFA
LYDDA
JERUSALEM
BETHLEHEM
DEAD SEA
BEERSHEBA
SODOM
EGYPT
FIRST HALF OF THE TOUR
SECOND HALF OF THE TOUR

As the train took them south towards Beersheba the country became wild and desolate. Very occasionally they saw a small village where the barren soil was being laboriously cultivated.

Alison said, " Haven't I read about Beersheba in the Bible? "

" I expected that question," their father replied, " so I looked it up. It's mentioned several times in the Old Testament. The first is in Genesis, chapter 21, verse 27, to the end of the chapter. Abraham dug a well and named the place Beersheba. Read it and see."

It was very hot in Beersheba. When they had signed the hotel register they went out to see the town which, John noted down, had a population of thirty-two thousand people.

" The place seems to be full of Arabs! " John said.

" And camels, too, and some of the Arabs are riding *lovely* horses," he continued.

" Beersheba is the capital of the Negev," his father explained, " and it's the main town for the Bedouin Arabs. They live a wandering life in the south of Israel here. They move about grazing their sheep, and they live a hard, simple life in tents."

" Look, it's market day! " Alison exclaimed pointing. " Let's go."

The market was a busy, bustling place. People argued over prices, examined goods, or stood chatting. Camels were tethered near their owners' goods. There were piles of melons, pomegranates, grapes, pumpkins, baskets of scarlet peppers and spices; saddles, rope, cloth, knives, pots and pans—a wonderful assortment of wares.

After dinner they went for a stroll in old Beersheba to enjoy the cool of the evening after the very hot day. They sat at a table outside a café and ate ice-creams. The moon shone brightly, haunting Eastern music came from a near-by window, and Arabs walked softly past in their sandals. It was a magic evening, and all rather mysterious.

John was watching the people, and suddenly he asked his father a question. "I thought the Arabs weren't friendly with Israel? Yet these Arabs, and the ones we've seen all over Israel, seem to be quite at home."

"They *are* at home, John, because this is their country. They are full citizens of Israel, the same as everyone else. They can have the same free schooling, the medical services, and so on. They have the vote at elections, and there are Arabs in the Israel Parliament, or Knesset. Unfortunately, the Arab countries on Israel's borders are all hostile. Israel only asks to be left in peace."

The next day they hired a car to take them to the Dead Sea, a wonderful drive of fifty miles eastwards from Beer-sheba. At first the road ran across the rolling desert, barren of all life. Then it wound its way downhill in gentle curves through a wilderness of rocks.

"Now you can understand what they mean in the Bible by the 'wilderness'," said their father.

He stopped and got out to take a photograph. Alison and John got out, too.

"Goodness!" Alison exclaimed. "Isn't it *hot*!"

"You could almost fry an egg on the ground!" agreed John.

" We seem to be going downhill all the time," John remarked, as they drove on towards the Dead Sea.

" We certainly are going downhill, John! In ten miles we drop from 1,800 feet *above* sea level to the Dead Sea which is 1,290 feet *below*. "

Suddenly they went round a bend and their father pulled up. Alison and John gasped at the grandeur of the scene. Below them was the Dead Sea, a great lake of brilliant blue between the tawny mountain crags. The water was absolutely still, gleaming in the sunshine.

" There it is! " their father said, after a silence. " The Dead Sea, fed by the River Jordan, and it is fifty miles long and nine miles wide. The lowest spot on earth! "

" Can we have a swim? " Alison asked.

" Yes, of course you can," her father replied, with a twinkle in his eyes.

They drove down to the edge of the sea and Alison and John changed quickly, eager to get into the water because they were so hot. They waded in and struck out.

Alison exclaimed. " I can't *sink*! The water holds me up! "

" Me, too! " John shouted. They laughed and splashed each other until Alison got some water in her mouth. She pulled a face and spat it out quickly. " Ugh! " she cried. " It's ever so salty! "

When they were lying on their towels after the swim their father explained. " The Dead Sea has no outlet," he said, " and it's so hot here that the water evaporates very quickly. So the salt and chemicals in the water are very strong—and you just can't sink! And there are no fish! They have built an enormous factory at the southern end, near the site of the ancient city of Sodom, to extract the valuable chemicals from the water."

As they drove along the edge of the Dead Sea their father told them some of the Bible stories connected with it. They saw a rock said to be the 'pillar of salt' into which Lot's wife was changed, when she disobeyed and looked back as she fled from the destruction of Sodom and Gomorrah. They saw the cave where David is supposed to have hidden from the wrath of Saul. They also went near to the caves where the Dead Sea scrolls were discovered by the shepherd boy in 1947.

With more notes written down in John's book, they turned back and drove uphill through the wilderness and then across the desert to Beersheba. The next morning they left by train, northwards again, for Jerusalem.

In the taxi from the station to their hotel, Alison and John looked out for their first impression of Jerusalem, the most historic city in the world. It was not at all what they had expected. There was nothing ancient or historic looking. They were driving along a fine, broad road lined with trees, with impressive new buildings on each side. There were gardens gay with flowers.

" This is only a part of the modern city of Jerusalem," their father explained, seeing that they were puzzled. " You'll see the old city from the terrace of our hotel. The new city is only a hundred years old, built outside the walls of old Jerusalem. It is the capital of Israel, the centre of government, and it is here Parliament meets. Jerusalem is the very heart of Israel."

When they got out of the taxi at their hotel Alison looked round and sighed. " So this is really Jerusalem," she said, " and we're here! "

Modern Jerusalem

" Well, John, what are your impressions of Jerusalem? " his father asked, when they had seen something of the city.

" It's a very large and rather confusing place," he replied, " a sort of patchwork of old and new."

" Is it true the new city was begun by an Englishman? " Alison asked.

" Quite true. About a hundred years ago a wealthy Englishman, Sir Moses Montefiore, spent his life and fortune helping Jews all over the world. Because the old city was so crowded, he built a small village outside the walls. Jews came from all over the world to live here, and the village grew into this great, straggling city. There are ' colonies,' separate parts for separate nationalities, and they say there are more than four hundred synagogues."

" I love the pinky stone of all the buildings," said Alison.

" It's quarried from the hills around here, Alison. That's why it blends with the countryside so well."

Their father took them to the top of the tall tower of the Y.M.C.A. building, and they looked over the hills and valleys towards the little town of Bethlehem, where Jesus was born. They went to Mount Zion, where it is believed David was buried; and where the Last Supper was held, when Our Lord was betrayed by Judas Iscariot.

That evening they were on the terrace of their hotel. The setting sun gilded the ancient walls of old Jerusalem, and they gazed at it with awe.

"That's a wonderful sight," their father said. " The City of David! For thirty-three centuries Jerusalem has suffered—war, sieges and earthquakes. She was laid desolate by Nebuchadnezzar and by the Roman Emperor Hadrian. It was there that Our Lord was crucified! Jerusalem, the Eternal City! "

View of Old Jerusalem

" When we go into the Old City," their father said, " we say good-bye to Israel. You see, Old Jerusalem isn't part of Israel. It's in the Kingdom of Jordan."

" But that seems strange! " John said.

" Political things are difficult to explain, John. But there it is! You'll find the people of Jordan very friendly. They take great care of all the places sacred to the Christians."

When they were actually in the streets of Old Jerusalem, Alison and John walked as if they were in a dream; it was all so wonderful. The narrow, steep streets, often made of shallow steps, were crowded. Donkeys with panniers pushed through the crowds. Little old shops displayed their wares, and through narrow doorways they had glimpses of little courtyards which might have been just the same when Jesus came to Jerusalem as a boy, or when He was brought to be crucified.

They walked slowly up the *Via Dolorosa*, the steep, winding street along which Jesus carried the great, heavy cross. They saw the 'Stations of the Cross' where He stopped on His way to the crucifixion.

Their father took them to the Church of the Holy Sepulchre built round the place where it is believed the tomb of Jesus was and from which He rose from the dead.

The church was a number of buildings, built by different sects of the Christian faith on this most holy of places. In the centre was a circular chapel covering the tomb itself.

A street in Old Jerusalem

As they wandered around Old Jerusalem, their father said, "There's an important point you must remember, Jerusalem is sacred to three different faiths. Do you know which they are?"

"The Christians," said Alison, "because Jesus was crucified here."

"The Jews, because Jerusalem was their capital in Old Testament days," John added.

"Right, and the third is the Mohammedans. They believe that the prophet Mohammed was carried up to the heavens from Jerusalem in a dream, by the angel Gabriel. Come, we'll go and see the 'Dome of Rock', built over the rock from which he was taken up."

They went into a great, open courtyard, one side of which was the wall of the city. They saw two lovely mosques, one of them topped by the famous dome. Inside they saw it was covered with ancient mosaic work.

As they stood looking across at the Mount of Olives from the wall of the courtyard, their father said, "This court is the site of the great temple of King Solomon!"

The most moving experience of all was when they went to the Garden of Gethsemane. Their father read aloud the story from the Bible, beginning at verse 36 in the 26th chapter of St. Matthew:

"*Then cometh Jesus with them unto a place called Gethsemane, and saith unto the disciples, Sit ye here, while I go and pray yonder.*"

When he had finished reading the story they walked among the trees, and looked at the walls of Jerusalem, each of them fully occupied with their own thoughts. Later they went to the 'Chapel of the Ascension' on the Mount of Olives. It is built over the place from which it is believed Our Lord ascended unto heaven.

The Garden of Gethsemene

In the car which was taking them the five miles from Jerusalem to Bethlehem, their father said, " We've been thinking about the Crucifixion and Resurrection of Our Lord in Jerusalem, the *end* of the story of Jesus. Now we are going to the place where that story began, to the place we think about at Christmas."

John asked, " Jesus lived as a boy in Nazareth in Galilee. How was it He was born in Bethlehem? "

" Don't you know that? " Alison said. " Joseph, the father of Jesus, had to go from Nazareth to Bethlehem to pay a special tax to the king, because Bethlehem was his home town. And Jesus was born while he and Mary were down here."

" That's how it was, John," his father said. " But Bethlehem is famous apart from being the birthplace of Jesus. It was the home of David when he was young; you know, the shepherd boy who slew the champion of the Philistines, Goliath, with a stone from his sling. Later David became king."

" And he wrote the Psalms! " said Alison.

Their father asked the driver to take them to the ' Field of the Shepherds ' before they went into Bethlehem itself. It was a wonderful experience to see the very field where the shepherds had been watching their sheep on that very first Christmas of all.

The children stood gazing round at the countryside, which was the same as the shepherds saw, while their father read the story from the Gospel of St. Luke, chapter 2, beginning at verse 8. "*And there were in the same country shepherds abiding in the field, keeping watch over their flock by night.*" . . .

It was an experience Alison and John would never forget.

Bethlehem is a prosperous well-built town, standing among vineyards, with good houses and shops. Many of the shops were selling souvenirs, made of mother-of-pearl, olive wood and stone. They bought some to take home. They saw schools and convents and the usual busy *bazaar*. The main feature was the ' Church of the Nativity ', built to enshrine the actual birthplace of Our Lord.

" The first church round the birthplace was built by Constantine the Great," their father told them, as they looked at the church. " That was in the year 330 A.D. Two hundred years later it was enlarged by the Emperor Justinian."

John wrote down these facts, and then they went inside. The " Grotto of the Nativity ' was in the middle of the church, with two sets of steps leading down to it. In the centre of the marble paving was a star, and round it was inscribed *Hic de Virgine Maria, Jesus Christus natus est.* Alison translated the Latin in a whisper, " Here of the Virgin Mary, Jesus Christ was born." At this most sacred spot they knelt and prayed.

They went down some steps to see three tombs of Fathers of the Church, who died fifteen-hundred years ago. One of them was Saint Jerome, and they went to see the chapel which was once the simple cell where he made his great translation of the scriptures into Latin.

When they went outside into the bright sunlight, their father looked at them, smiled, and said, " Well, what have you got to say about all *that*? "

Alison shook her head. " I don't think I could find words to describe how wonderful it all is," she said.

When they had explored Bethlehem thoroughly, they motored back to Jerusalem and went on a further twenty miles to Jericho. The road after Jerusalem was through a hot, barren wilderness, for it was in the Valley of the Dead Sea; indeed Jericho is only five miles north of the Dead Sea.

" Look, that must be Jericho! " Alison cried, pointing ahead to a cluster of white, flat-topped houses amid palm trees and green pasture.

" You see how good wells of sweet water change the desert," said her father.

They drove through orange and lemon groves, and past plantations of bananas, figs, and pineapples. When they had settled in their hotel, they enjoyed a long drink of iced lemonade after the very hot and dusty drive.

" Just outside the town is a mound," their father said, " which covers the remains of the oldest city on earth. Archæologists have done a lot of excavation here at Jericho and they date the first city as 6,000 B.C. ! They found signs of a civilisation which is older than anything else ever discovered. There have been several cities of Jericho—this one was built by the Crusaders eight-hundred years ago."

" Jericho comes into the Bible a lot, doesn't it? " asked Alison.

" Yes, the prophet Elisha dug a well here, and it was a city which Joshua captured."

Their father took them for a walk around Jericho, and they were fascinated by the thought that it's history stretched back to the very earliest days of man.

Outskirts of Jericho

After two days in Jericho, they left early in the morning by car for the forty-mile drive eastwards to Amman, the capital of Jordan. They got out of the car where the road crossed the River Jordan, and looked at the river which is so famous in the Bible.

There was not much time to spare in Amman, because they had to catch a train to take them north to Damascus. The one-hundred-and-twenty mile journey took them out of Jordan into Syria. In spite of the blinds over the windows, it was very hot, and they were glad when the train drew up at the noisy, bustling station of Damascus.

It proved to be a very large, busy Arab city, with donkeys and camels in plenty. Their father took them to a narrow street, covered by a domed roof. There were archways along both sides, with shutters; these were shops.

" Alison," her father said, " take your Bible and turn up the Acts of the Apostles, chapter 9, and read us verses 10 and 11."

She opened her Bible and read the two verses aloud. In the second verse she read, "*Arise, and go into the street which is called Straight*."

" And this," her father said, " is the actual street which is called Straight! It was on a journey to Damascus that St. Paul was converted by a vision, and it was in this town that he began his ministry. He was imprisoned, and escaped over the walls in a basket. It's a grand story; read it for yourselves."

The next day they went to the Airport, got into an airliner, and flew off. Their route was via Cyprus, Athens, Rome and London. Their father had taken many photographs, Alison had a store of sketches, and John's notebook was packed with facts; but most important, their heads were full of memories, memories they would never lose, of ' The Holy Land '.

A street in Damascus

AIR ROUTE TRAVELLED
BY ALISON AND JOHN